PRENATAL TESTS

by
Agneta Sutton

*All booklets are published thanks to the
generous support of the members of the
Catholic Truth Society*

CATHOLIC TRUTH SOCIETY
PUBLISHERS TO THE HOLY SEE

CONTENTS

The Linacre Centre

The Linacre Centre is the only Catholic institution of its kind specialising in the field of healthcare ethics in Great Britain and Ireland. As such, it provides a unique service to the Catholic community in these islands, and more particularly to Catholics working in the field of healthcare. The Centre also exists to assist the teaching authorities within the Church in addressing bioethical issues, and to communicate and defend the Church's moral teaching in debates over public policy and legislation in the United Kingdom.

The Centre has built up a bioethics library of over 6,000 titles. It has three research fellows who are able to give time and thought to new and difficult issues in bioethics and it is also able to call upon the help of a range of experts in medicine, law, philosophy, theology and history. The Centre is affiliated to Ave Maria School of Law. It publishes reports, organises conferences and lectures, and does consultancy work for individuals and for other organisations.

The Centre can be contacted at 38 Circus Road, London NW8 9SE, by phone at (020) 7266 7410, or via our website at *www.linacre.org*.

INTRODUCTION

The development of prenatal tests started some thirty years ago. This was with the use of **amniocentesis**[1] to detect **rhesus disease** in the unborn child in order to determine the need for early delivery. Today there are many other prenatal testing techniques in addition to amniocentesis. And the amniocentesis technique itself is used to detect a variety of conditions in the unborn child besides rhesus disease.

Indeed, pregnancy has come under increasing medical control. This medicalisation of pregnancy has both good and bad aspects. On the positive side, pregnancy and childbirth have become much safer for the mother. Likewise, infant mortality has decreased. Compared with the past, there is also a greater awareness of the nature of the unborn child. This is not only on the part of doctors and midwives but also on the part of parents. The ultrasound scan, which allows the mother to see the unborn child, has been especially influential. The unborn child seems somehow more real when it can be seen. On the negative side, today pregnancy is treated almost as a disease. And the availability of tests to detect foetal abnormality has led to a subtle social pressure both on

---

[1] The first time a technical term such as this occurs it will be indicated in bold letters. The term will also appear in the glossary at the end of the booklet.

pregnant mothers and on clinicians to prevent the birth of disabled children by means of abortion. Both the medical profession and pregnant women now see prenatal diagnosis as a necessary part of prenatal care. Yet the choice with which the mother is faced, if a foetal abnormality is found, is a cause of much distress and a matter of grave moral concern. Thus, while some tests are undertaken with the aim of promoting a safe pregnancy and birth, there are a number of tests the primary aim of which is to detect foetal abnormality with a view to avoiding the birth of a disabled child.

This booklet explains the aims and risks of prenatal tests as well as the Church's teaching about the sanctity of life and the dignity of the family. It also looks at the psychological impact on the pregnant woman and at the social consequences of tests serving as a preamble to abortion on grounds of foetal abnormality.

The first chapter presents two case studies. These provide typical examples of the circumstances under which pregnant mothers are offered special and not altogether risk-free prenatal tests, such as amniocentesis, in order to detect foetal abnormality. These kinds of test are not offered to all pregnant mothers, but only to those who are thought to be at special risk. Other tests are offered routinely to all pregnant mothers to check the health of mother and child.

In the second chapter the various tests offered are described. It is explained whether their primary aim is to promote a safe pregnancy and delivery or, rather, to detect foetal abnormality in order to avoid the birth of a disabled child. The risks of different tests are also explained. While most abortions are undertaken because the mother feels she cannot cope with pregnancy and ensuing motherhood, today a fair number of abortions are undertaken in order to avoid the birth of a disabled child.

Following this overview of the medical facts, the Church's teaching is set out in the third chapter. With reference to relevant Church documents, the reader is told why the Church advocates respect for human life at all stages from **conception (fertilisation)** until natural death. Here the Church's teaching on the sanctity of life and on the dignity of motherhood and of the family is explained.

In the fourth chapter various arguments presented in favour of abortion on grounds of foetal abnormality are examined. Many parents, doctors and midwives would say that it would be better for a disabled child not to be born or that the birth of a disabled child would constitute too much of a burden on the family. Arguments such as these are discussed in relation to the right to life of the child who, as a gift from God and created in the image of God, should be welcomed irrespective of his or her disability.

The booklet closes with a general discussion of the ethical and social implications of prenatal diagnosis in order to avoid the birth of disabled children. While some of the tests offered to pregnant women have made pregnancy less risky than in the past, several of the new technologies both reflect and promote what Pope John Paul II has called the culture of death. In addition, they reflect a certain naïve optimism insofar as they give the impression that we are about to eliminate illness and disability. Disability and illness are part of the human condition. We are mortal creatures. No medical technologies can alter this. New genetic mutations arise constantly giving rise to new cases of genetic disease. Besides, many conditions are caused by environmental factors beyond our control.

More important, measures to promote the general health of the population are welcome only if they are humane. A society that fails to welcome the disabled and the ill is an inhuman society. In such a society nobody is ultimately safe.

TWO CASE STUDIES

Mary

Mary is aged 36 and pregnant with her second child.

The risk of having a child with **Down's syndrome** gradually increases with age. Mary at 36 has had a blood test to make sure that she is not carrying a baby with Down's syndrome. She had been told that it was a good idea to have the test. Mary already has a child, a little boy, who is three years old and healthy. And she feels that all is well this time too. But the test result has just come back and the doctor said that it indicates that her baby might have Down's syndrome and that she should discuss with her husband whether she wants an amniocentesis to find out whether the baby really is affected. She is now 16 weeks pregnant and feels that she had better make up her mind fast. And she knows that the purpose of the test is to allow an abortion, if the child is affected. However, she has also been informed that the test brings with it an increased risk of miscarriage.

Neither Mary nor her husband would want an abortion. And of course, they do not want to risk losing a healthy child as a result of amniocentesis. But they also fear that a baby with Down's syndrome would not have a happy life, though they have heard that such children are often of a happy and good-natured disposition. As the days go by, Mary gets more and more nervous about the situation. In the end she decides to have the test.

She is scared but goes ahead with amniocentesis. Luckily, the test shows no problems and she does not lose her baby as a result of it. Afterwards Mary feels both relieved and angry. Why did she have to be faced with such an awful choice? After all, the risk of having a Down's syndrome baby at her age is small. She would rather not have had this worry. She feels that the offer of amniocentesis spoilt some of the pleasure of her pregnancy. However, she is determined to put the thought of the test behind her and continue as if nothing had happened.

Jenny

Jenny aged 29 has a child with **cystic fibrosis** and is pregnant again.

Jenny is in the 7th week of her second pregnancy. She is worried. This is because her first child, a little girl of six, has cystic fibrosis (CF). She knows that there is a 25% risk that her second child is also affected. She has spoken to a counsellor about it. And she has been told that, if she wants to know whether the child she is carrying is affected, she can choose between **chorion villus sampling** in the 12th week or an amniocentesis in the 16th week. It has also been pointed out to her that the advantage of the former test over the amniocentesis is that it is performed earlier. This would allow her to have an abortion earlier, should the child be affected. The disadvantage of chorion villus sampling, compared with amniocentesis, is that it carries a greater risk of miscarriage. Because of the greater risk of miscarriage, Jenny decides that she does not want chorion villus sampling. But she remains hesitant about amniocentesis.

She does not want a second child in need of special medical attention and whose life expectancy is significantly reduced. No, she does not want any other child of hers to be in that condition. On the other hand, she knows that great medical progress has been made in the last twenty years and that, as a result, the prospects of children with CF have greatly improved. For example, she has read about experiments with gene therapy. And while she knows that gene therapy is not at present a realistic option, she believes that in the future it might be. Hence, she feels that, even if her second child were affected, it might be wrong not to give it a chance.

Jenny and her husband discuss the matter at length. In the end, they decide to say that they want to keep their baby. However, when Jenny talks to her counsellor again, she is told that she might want an amniocentesis either for reassurance or to prepare herself for a second affected child. Like Mary, she is also told that the amniocentesis carries a certain risk of miscarriage. But, having decided to keep the baby, Jenny insists that she does not want an amniocentesis. She now wants to leave the matter in the hands of God.

TECHNIQUES, AIMS AND RISKS

Tests to promote the health of mother and baby

Non-invasive tests

There are a number of regular non-invasive tests that are aimed at ensuring a healthy pregnancy. These tests, which incur no risks, include regular checks of:

- Blood pressure
- Urine glucose
- Urine protein
- Foetal heartbeat - beginning when the baby's heart is developed enough to be heard
- Ultrasound

Blood pressure

The mother's blood volume increases in pregnancy. Together with the foetal blood circulation, this increases the demand on the mother's heart. It is therefore important to regularly measure her blood pressure to make sure that she is well and that her baby is not exposed to any risks. Hypertension in combination with swelling and protein in the urine indicate that the mother is affected by pre-eclampsia, a condition that needs prompt medical attention.

Urine glucose and urine protein

The pregnant mother will regularly be asked for urine samples. The presence of glucose in the urine is an indication of gestational diabetes. This could make the baby grow larger than normal. It could also affect its health adversely. However, pregnancy-induced diabetes may be treated by a special diet. In some cases the mother might have to take insulin. The condition usually disappears after delivery. Protein in the urine indicates that the mother has a kidney problem or an infection. As noted above, it could also be a sign of pre-eclampsia.

Ultrasound

The ultrasound scan is painless and is widely believed to be harmless. Even though it can be performed at any time, it is often performed around mid-pregnancy, that is, some time between the 16th and the 23rd week. An instrument is passed over the mother's abdomen and a picture of the baby is produced on a screen. The main aim of the scan is to determine the gestational age of the baby. Indeed, the scan is more accurate than dating from the mother's last menstrual cycle. The scan also shows whether there is more than one child.

Occasionally foetal disabling conditions are picked up. If this happens, or if other tests point to a foetal disability, a more detailed ultrasound examination may be made. This might be with a view to assessing the best time and mode of delivery and whether the baby would need special attention immediately after birth. But it could also be with a view to offering the mother the option of an abortion.

Ultrasound is also used for visual guidance in connection with invasive tests such as amniocentesis or chorionic villus sampling.

Invasive tests

- First trimester blood sampling
- Second trimester blood sampling

In the first trimester the mother may have blood tests to determine the following:

- Blood iron content
- Blood type and **Rhesus** compatibility
- Presence of antibodies to the **HIV virus**

Blood iron content

This is important for haemoglobin, and thus for the delivery of oxygen to the foetus. If the mother's blood iron content is low (that is, if she is anaemic), she may be given iron supplements.

Blood type and Rh compatibility

It is important to know the mother's blood type and especially whether she is rhesus negative. This is because the mother who belongs to the rhesus-negative blood group and whose husband belongs to the rhesus-positive group is at risk of developing anti-bodies directed at rhesus-positive foetuses. And this could cause foetal anaemia and mental retardation (rhesus disease). The risk increases with each pregnancy. However, today rhesus-negative mothers are treated to minimise the risk of an adverse immune response.

Antibodies to the HIV virus

With the help of modern drugs, the risk of passing on HIV to the child can now be significantly reduced. Thus mothers who think that they might be HIV positive are advised to be tested for the virus.

Tests to detect babies with disabilities and enable abortion

Invasive tests: mother only

In the second trimester (around the 16th to 18th week) the mother may be offered a blood test to measure three factors:

- **Alpha-fetoprotein (AFP)**
- **Human chorionic gonadotropin (hCG)**
- **Oestriol**

These are the kind of tests that the pregnant mother might wish to refuse. They do not promote the health of the mother or the baby. They are undertaken with a view to further tests aimed at the detection of foetal abnormality so that an abortion can be offered.

AFP

AFP is a protein that is made by the baby. In neural tube defects the baby's skin is not intact, which allows larger than normal amounts of AFP to escape. Hence, larger amounts than normal are measured in the mother's blood. This is why high levels of AFP indicate that the baby may have a neural tube defect. A detailed ultrasound examination may be carried out to confirm this finding. By contrast, in Down's syndrome, AFP is decreased.

hCG

A high hCG level in combination with a low AFP level suggests that the baby may have a chromosomal abnormality. The most common condition of this kind is Down's syndrome.

Oestriol

Low levels of oestriol could be an indication that the baby is unwell. In particular, it might have Down's syndrome or a neural tube defect.

Invasive tests: both mother and child

Performed with a view to detecting foetal disability in order to offer the mother the choice of abortion. Tests that are invasive in regard to both mother and baby carry a risk of losing or damaging the baby.

- Amniocentesis
- Chorionic villus sampling

Amniocentesis

This is the most common invasive test, apart from maternal blood sampling. The test is usually performed between the 14th to the 18th week of pregnancy. A sample of the amniotic fluid surrounding the baby - who floats around within the amniotic sac in the womb - is obtained by inserting a needle through the mother's abdomen. The procedure is performed using ultrasound guidance, in order to avoid injuring the baby. The amniotic fluid contains both cells and chemicals of foetal origin, which may be examined to see whether the foetus is well. For the purpose of examination the cells are usually cultured to obtain a sufficient number. This takes time and is why parents often have to wait two to three weeks for the test results to come through. However, with new ways of obtaining test results from smaller quantities of cells, results can sometimes be obtained within a couple of days.

The risk of an amniocentesis causing a miscarriage is estimated at about 2% at 11 weeks, 1% at 16 weeks. However, the risk may be greater as these estimates solely relate to miscarriages recorded within two weeks of the test. In other words, the risk of a miscarriage as a result of the test is significant. Other possible side-effects include cramp, bleeding, leaking of amniotic fluid and infection, limb deformity in the baby and lung problems, especially in the case of early amniocentesis.

Amniocentesis is mostly used to detect chromosomal abnormality, and the most common type of chromosomal abnormality is Down's syndrome. As the risk of carrying a baby affected by Down's syndrome increases with age, mothers over 35 are routinely offered an hCG test to see whether they are at risk. Often younger mothers too are offered the test. Whatever the mother's age, if the hCG indicates that there might be a problem, the mother will be offered an amniocentesis, which is a more accurate test. But it should be noted that no test is a hundred percent accurate.

The amniocentesis can also be used to detect a number of hereditary sex-linked conditions such as **Duchenne muscular dystrophy, haemophilia factor VIII** and **haemophilia factor IX**, as well as single-gene conditions such as **cystic fibrosis, sickle-cell disease, thalassaemias** and **Tay-Sachs disease**. Thus the mother at special risk of having a baby affected by a hereditary condition may also be offered an amniocentesis. There may be different reasons for thinking that the mother is at special risk. In addition, the test may be used to detect neural tube disorders such as **spina bifida**.

As to hereditary conditions, the mother or father may be affected by a dominant genetic condition such as **Huntington disease**. The risk of inheriting a dominant condition from an affected parent is 50%. In the particular case of Huntington disease, the disease does not surface until the individual reaches middle-age, which means that an affected parent-to-be would not know about his or her condition. That there is a risk is normally known because there is a family history of the disease. However in this kind of situation, many parents-to-be would prefer not to test the child. For if the child tests positive, it means that the parent in whose family the disease runs is also affected by the condition. Moreover, why test the unborn child for a condition that would not affect it until much later in life?

Another situation in which the mother would be thought to be at special risk is when she already has a child affected by a genetic condition. In chapter 1 the case of a mother with a child affected by cystic fibrosis was presented. This is a recessive condition. Such conditions may be inherited by children from their parents, even if neither parent is affected. Sickle-cell disease and the thalassaemias are other diseases of this kind. They may be inherited if both parents are carriers of a faulty copy of the gene associated with the condition (even though they themselves are not affected). If both parents are carriers of a faulty copy of the gene in question, the risk of having an affected baby is 25%.

Finally, certain population groups are more frequently affected than others by some of these recessive diseases. This has led to the establishment of special screening programmes in many places. Thus adults who are considering parenthood or couples who are expecting a child may be offered blood tests to determine whether they are carriers. For example, in some areas in Britain couples of European origin who are expecting a child are screened to see whether they are carriers of cystic fibrosis. This is because cystic fibrosis is the most common recessive condition among people of European origin. If both parents are carriers of the faulty gene, the pregnant mother is offered an amniocentesis.

The thalassaemias are most common among people of Mediterranean origin. People of African origin are at risk of sickle-cell disease. Hence, they may be offered screening for this condition, while Ashkenazi Jews (from central and eastern Europe) may be screened for Tay-Sachs disease, since this disease is common in this population group.

Those who have prenatal tests should, however, be aware that no test is foolproof. In the case of Down's syndrome, it is estimated that the ultrasound tests will detect about 70% of all babies with Down's syndrome. More important, tests may falsely indicate that the baby is affected by the condition. The risk of wrongly diagnosing Down's syndrome by means of amniocentesis is estimated at about 5% to 8%. In other words, 5 to 8 times out of hundred the test falsely indicates that the baby is affected by Down's syndrome. This suggests that a significant number of those babies who are aborted because the amniocentesis indicates that they may have Down's syndrome are, in fact, healthy!

Chorionic villus sampling

This procedure is sometimes used instead of an amniocentesis to detect chromosomal or genetic disorders. The test, which carries a somewhat higher risk of miscarriage than an amniocentesis, is performed earlier than amniocentesis, usually between the 10th and 12th week. No culturing of the tissue is required, and so the results of the test are obtained within a few days. As for the risks of the procedure, besides miscarriage, the other side-effects are similar to those associated with amniocentesis.

The test itself involves taking a small amount of the **chorionic tissue** surrounding the unborn child. Because the placenta derives from the foetus, and not from the mother, it contains foetal cells. The tissue is obtained either by inserting a needle through the mother's abdomen under ultrasound guidance or by means of a fine tube passed through the vagina.

Those who are in favour of abortion on grounds of foetal handicap often argue that the advantage of this test compared with amniocentesis is that it may be carried out earlier. The earlier the mother is tested, the earlier she can have an abortion, if her child is affected.

A specialist test with therapeutic and non-therapeutic potential

Cordocentesis

Foetal blood sampling, or cordocentesis, may be carried out from the 18th week onwards. This test involves taking blood from the umbilical cord and is therefore invasive with regard to the child and carries a risk of miscarriage. As in the case of an amniocentesis, a needle is passed through the maternal abdomen under ultrasound guidance. The test may be used to diagnose chromosomal disorders or single-gene disorders as well as viral infection or anaemia. It may also be used to determine the baby's blood group and whether mother and baby are rhesus-factor compatible. If they are not rhesus-factor compatible and the baby is affected by foetal rhesus disease, the technique may be used to give the unborn child a blood transfusion. In other words, this technique may be used for therapeutic as well as diagnostic purposes.

Like amniocentesis and chorionic villus sampling, cordocentesis carries a certain risk of miscarriage.

Type of test	Diagnosable conditions	Stage of pregnancy	Promotes health of mother and baby?
NON-INVASIVE			
ultrasound scan	Down's syndrome	11-12 weeks	no
ultrasound scan	dates, twins, malformations	16-23 weeks	yes, often but not always
INVASIVE: MOTHER ONLY			
second trimester blood sampling	Down's syndrome neural tube disorders	12-24 weeks	no
INVASIVE: BOTH MOTHER AND FOETUS			
amniocentesis	Down's syndrome, chromosomal conditions single-gene conditions neural tube disorders	14-18 weeks	no
chorionic villus sampling	Down's syndrome other chromosomal conditions, single-gene conditions	12-13 weeks	no
cordocentesis	Mainly for treating foetal rhesus disease	18 weeks onwards	yes

Preimplantation diagnosis

While most prenatal testing is undertaken during pregnancy, it is now also possible to test for a number of conditions as well for the sex of the child or even its tissue type before it implants in the womb. Needless to say, this kind of testing can only be undertaken in the context of ***in vitro* fertilisation (IVF)**, where the embryo is created outside the mother's body. The test involves taking a couple of cells from the embryo and examining them. If the embryo is found to be free of the suspected genetic disease, or if it is of the right sex to avoid a **sex-linked disease**, or of the right tissue type to treat an older sibling, it can then be transferred to the mother's womb.

The reason why sex-linked diseases, such as Duchenne muscular dystrophy, affect boys, but not often girls, is that they are recessive and linked to genes found on **X-chromosomes**. Our genes are carried on **chromosomes** in the nuclei of our cells. Human beings have 23 pairs of chromosomes. The chromosomes in the 23rd pair determine our sex and are indicated by the letters X and Y. Girls have two X-chromosomes, while boys have one X and one **Y-chromosome**. This means that when a girl has a faulty copy of a gene on one of her X-chromosomes, there is normally a healthy matching copy of the gene on the other X-chromosome. Hence, she is not affected, even if she carries a faulty gene. Boys, on the other hand, have a Y-chromosome and an X-chromosome. The Y-chromosome is smaller than the X-chromosome, which means that a faulty gene on the X-chromosome may not be matched by a healthy gene on the Y-chromosome. When a faulty recessive gene is not matched by a healthy gene, the child will be affected by a sex-linked disease. In the case of preimplantation diagnosis to determine the sex of the embryo, both healthy and affected male embryos are discarded.

Embryos who have an older sibling with a treatable condition may also be tested to see if after birth they could provide a cord blood or bone marrow transplant for the sibling. If their tissue would not be compatible, they are discarded, even if they themselves are healthy. Many embryos may be discarded before finding the right tissue match - a so-called 'saviour sibling'.

From the moral point of view, the most important consideration here is the loss of embryonic life which IVF involves even without such additional procedures as preimplantation diagnosis. Older mothers, who are at increased risk of having a child with a chromosomal condition, may be offered pre-implantation screening (PGS). This test is used to diagnose chromosomal conditions. Like PFD, it involves the removal of one or two cells from the embryo and testing them for abnormalities, in this case chromosomal abnormalities.

Moreover, procreation involving no union in the flesh of husband and wife is highly manipulative and a threat to human dignity. The child is treated as a product rather than as a gift, and the parents themselves become providers of raw material for its making. For this reason, and because of the loss of embryonic life involved, IVF is condemned by the Catholic Church.

As regards embryo loss, when a woman undergoes IVF treatment, a number of embryos are usually 'created' at the same time. One reason for this is to spare the woman burdensome treatment should she want to have embryos implanted on more than one occasion. Hence, the woman is given hormones to make her super-ovulate and produce many ripe eggs in the same menstrual cycle. But to avoid the risks attached to a multiple pregnancy with three or more babies, no more than two embryos may be implanted on the same occasion. This means that there will usually be a fair number of 'spare' embryos left over after IVF. These embryos may be stored, that is, frozen, for future IVF treatment. With the parents' permission, spare embryos may also be used for research or immediately destroyed.

THE CHURCH'S TEACHING

Is prenatal diagnosis morally acceptable? The document *Donum Vitae* of 1987 ('Instruction on respect for human life in its origin and on the dignity of procreation'), published by the Congregation for the Doctrine of the Faith, gives the following answer to this question:

> If prenatal diagnosis respects the life and integrity of the embryo and the human foetus and is directed towards its safeguarding or healing as an individual, then the answer is affirmative (*Donum Vitae*, para. I.2).

In other words, prenatal diagnosis is not morally acceptable if it is undertaken with a view to selective abortion on grounds of foetal abnormality. The procedure should serve such a purpose as detecting abnormality with a view to deciding on the best kind and timing of delivery, or treatment of the child in the womb if that is possible and indicated.

Donum Vitae also specifies that informed consent must be sought from the parents in order for a test to be justified. That is, the parents must have given their consent to the procedure after having received the information required to understand the risks and benefits involved.

It is further stated in *Donum Vitae* that the techniques employed must subject neither the mother nor the child to disproportionate risks. In other words, the potential benefits to the unborn child of subjecting it to a particular prenatal test must clearly outweigh the risks of harming either mother or child. As Pope John Paul II put it in an address to the Pro-Life Movement, if 'a degree of risk must be undertaken', the doctor must 'ensure that it is justified by a truly urgent need for the diagnosis and by the importance of the results that can be achieved by it for the benefit of the unborn child himself' (John Paul II, *'Discourse to Participants in the Pro-Life Movement Congress'*, 3 December 1982).

Evangelium Vitae

More recently, in his Encyclical Letter *Evangelium Vitae* ('The Gospel of Life') of 1995, John Paul II writes of prenatal diagnostic techniques:

> When they do not involve disproportionate risks for the child and the mother, and are meant to make possible early therapy or even to favour a serene and informed acceptance of the child not yet born, these techniques are morally licit. But since the possibilities of prenatal therapy are today still limited, it not infrequently happens that these techniques are used with a eugenic intention which accepts selective abortion in order to prevent the birth of children affected by various types of anomalies. Such an attitude is shameful and utterly reprehensible, since it presumes to measure the value of

a human life only within the parameters of 'normality' and physical well-being, thus opening the way to legitimising infanticide and euthanasia as well (*Evangelium Vitae*, para. 63).

The Pope also observes that the Church is close to parents who willingly, though with great suffering, accept severely disabled children.

Earlier in the Encyclical, John Paul II speaks more generally of the value of life:

> Life is always a good. This is an instinctive perception and a fact of experience, and man is called to grasp the profound reason why this is so.
>
> Why is life good? This question is found everywhere in the Bible, and from the very first pages it receives a powerful and amazing answer. The life which God gives man is quite different from the life of all other living creatures, inasmuch as man, although formed from the dust of the earth (*cf. Gn.* 2:7; 3:19; *Jb* 34:15; *Ps* 103:14, 104:29) is a manifestation of God in the world, a sign of His presence, a trace of His glory (*cf. Gn* 1:26-27; *Ps* 8:6) (*Evangelium Vitae*, para. 34).

In fact, the Catholic Church has always held that abortion is gravely wrong (see the booklet on abortion in this series). Life is a gift from God and so to be cherished and protected from the outset until natural death. Each human being is created in the image of God and for union with God and, as such, each person possesses the same human dignity. Each human being is also created for union and communion with neighbour, old and young, sick and healthy.

Letter to Families

In his *Letter to Families*, published in 1994, Pope John Paul II writes that not only is the divine likeness transmitted in human generation, but also the child is 'the first gift of the Creator to the creature' and an expression of God's self-giving (*Letter to Families*, Rome, 1994, para. 11). Thus the child, through whom parents become co-creators, is a divine gift in the image of God Himself and so truly precious and to be welcomed, cherished and nourished both physically and spiritually. Pope John Paul II tells us that each new human life is immensely valuable, since it is initiated and willed as something in His image by God Himself.

> Man's coming into being does not conform to the laws of biology alone, but also and directly to God's creative will, which is concerned with the genealogy of the sons and daughters of human families. God 'willed' man from the very beginning and God 'wills' him in every act of conception and every human birth. God 'wills' man as a being similar to himself, as a person (*Letter to Families*, para. 9).

Even if the medieval Church prescribed less severe penalties for early than for late abortion, the Church nonetheless always held that abortion, early as well as late, was gravely wrong.[2] In other words, abortion at all stages has always been regarded as contrary to the creative intentions of God. It has always been viewed as an interference with life, and thus as wrong, because life belongs to God.

Today, with increasing scientific knowledge, the Church makes no distinction of any kind between early and late abortion. It follows that prenatal diagnosis with the intention of having an abortion, if results confirm a foetal abnormality, is considered wrong by the Church irrespective of the timing of the abortion.

It should also be noted that *Donum Vitae* stresses that not only is it gravely wrong for the pregnant mother herself to undergo prenatal tests with a view to selective abortion if an abnormality is found, but, equally, it would be gravely wrong for her spouse, her relatives or any other person to recommend or press her to undergo prenatal tests with a view to selective abortion (*Donum Vitae*, I, 2). In other words, the document declares that doctors, midwives and counsellors who recommend prenatal tests in order to offer the woman the choice of an abortion are acting immorally.

The Catholic Church likewise condemns any programme of the civil or health authorities that promotes prenatal

---

[2] See Helen Watt's booklet *Abortion* in this series.

diagnosis with the aim of preventing births of disabled children. Thus the Catholic Church condemns programmes aimed at eliminating, for example, thalassaemias by means of extensive prenatal screening programmes, undertaken on the assumption that unborn children found to be affected by the condition will be aborted.

According to the Christian understanding of the child as a gift and of each human being as created in the image of God and in possession of the same human dignity, neither malformation nor genetic illness are grounds for discrimination. And this applies to the unborn as well as to the born. Each child is to be welcomed as a new member of the human family at large as well as of the intimate family at home. Each child is a gift to humankind and especially to its parents.

Familiaris Consortio

Pope John Paul II has also declared that the child has a right to be born within a family founded on marriage. Both in his Apostolic Exhortation *Familiaris Consortio*, published in 1981, and in his *Letter to Families*, published fourteen years later, he presents an understanding of the family and the parent-child relationship which favours procreation in that it sees the child as completing the relationship between husband and wife. Taking as his starting point that every child ought to be born within a family founded on a monogamous and indissoluble marriage, he writes that, for Christian spouses, the child represents 'the crowning of their own love' (*Letter to Families*, para. 9) and that, as 'a living reflection of their love, it is a permanent sign of conjugal unity and a living and inseparable synthesis of their being a father and a mother' (*Familiaris Consortio*, 1981, para. 14).

While Pope John Paul II sees procreation as a natural good insofar as it ensures the survival of the species, he also refers to it as cooperation with the creative activity of God. Indeed, overall, in the aforementioned two documents addressed to the family, there is a great emphasis on the importance of openness to life and biological fecundity *qua* biological and creative. But the Pope also insists that biological fecundity must go hand in hand with spiritual fecundity. Thus, speaking in line with a long tradition going back to St Thomas and beyond, he says that, for Christians, biological begetting must be coupled with spiritual begetting through a Christian education. For Pope John Paul II, this means that the Christian family should bear witness before society at large to God's creative, covenantal and salvific plans for man by welcoming and nourishing new human life and cultivating the fruits of the Holy Spirit, which are love for God and neighbour. In other words, Pope John Paul II argues for the value of the family both as a biological entity and as a spiritual community, bearing witness to God's love for mankind by means of Christian charity. He asks the Christian family to take up an evangelical and social mission. In *Familiaris Consortio* he states that 'the family has the mission to guard, reveal and communicate love, and this mission is the living reflection of and a real sharing in God's love for humanity and the love of Christ the Lord for the Church His bride' (*Familiaris Consortio*, para. 17).

Thus, in *Familiaris Consortio*, Pope John Paul II refers to the Christian family as the 'domestic Church'. In doing so he is telling us that the Christian family is an essential part of the Church and that, as such, it is called to contribute to the transformation of the earth and the renewal of the world. He says: 'in this way, while the Christian family is a fruit and sign of the supernatural fecundity of the Church, it stands also as a symbol, witness and participant of the Church's motherhood' (*Familiaris Consortio*, para. 49).

In a similar vein, Pope John Paul II speaks, in his *Letter to Families*, of the civilisation of love, as opposed to the civilisation of consumerism and utility. In the latter, he says, there reigns an attitude of self-centred individualism and consumerism, which depersonalises others and approaches them in an instrumental and manipulative way (*Letter to Families*, para. 1, paras. 14-15). These words are applicable not least to prenatal diagnosis aimed at the elimination of children with disability. The foetus tested and undergoing quality control is certainly depersonalised and treated in a manipulative way. Presenting an alternative way of life to that marked by self-centred individualism and consumerism, Pope John Paul II argues for neighbourly love and solidarity with others, especially the disadvantaged and weak within society. Among the latter are, of course, people born affected by disability or genetic illness. But also among them are unborn members of the human family similarly affected by illness or disability. The civilisation of love is represented by an attitude which - springing from the power of grace - entails respect for other people as persons created in the image of God and for God, and thus possessing inherent value and dignity, irrespective of their particular skills or failings and irrespective of their abilities or disabilities.

On Pope John Paul II's understanding, then, the Christian family, as a fundamental pillar within society, based on the rock of monogamous and indissoluble marriage, has an important role to play. This is both in the loving protection, care and education of children and in the service of society as a witness to the Gospel call for love of God and neighbour. And among our neighbours he counts especially the weakest members of society, born and unborn.

Mulieris Dignitatem

In his apostolic letter *Mulieris Dignitatem* ('The Dignity of Women',1988), Pope John Paul II likewise speaks at length about the important role of parents and the dignity of parenthood as a reflection of God's own creativity and self-giving love. He says that: 'the eternal mystery of generation, which is in God Himself, the one Triune God (cf. Eph 3:14-15), is reflected in the woman's motherhood and in the man's fatherhood' (*Mulieris Dignitatem*, para. 17). That is to say, the child is the fruit of the mutual self-giving of man and woman. On this understanding, then, fatherhood and motherhood serve as pointers to the inner self-giving relational life of the Trinity and to God's love of mankind.

Laying special stress on the dignity of motherhood, Pope John Paul II shows that the gift of motherhood involves a particular responsibility and a particular pleasure and pain. He shows that by entrusting the weakest member of the human family to the care of woman, God has shown her a special honour. And this is an honour that calls for a self-giving openness to life that is totally selfless and totally welcoming of the child. It calls for an unconditional love and total commitment to the child as a gift to be cherished and protected both while it grows inside the womb and afterwards.

Pope John Paul II especially emphasises that motherhood, as the fruit of man's and woman's mutual self-giving in marriage, implies 'a special openness to the new person', a special gift of self on the part of the woman. This is for the reason that, while the upbringing of a child normally involves many sacrifices on the part of both parents, the woman's physical self-giving reflects a special preparedness to give. However, in return, she also experiences a special pleasure in the realisation that in giving she is also receiving. This is why Pope John Paul II also says that the words of Eve at the birth of her first-born express the joy of every mother at her discovery of 'sharing in the great mystery of creation' (*Ibid.*).

A Critical Examination of Arguments in Favour of Selective Abortion

Parental pity

Parents naturally want healthy children. This is not only so that they can be proud of their children, but also, and primarily, because they do not want their children to suffer. Many parents would rather take the place of their children if they saw them suffer. Hence, a major reason why pregnant mothers and their spouses may ask for prenatal diagnosis and opt for an abortion, if their child is found to be affected by a serious condition - such as sickle-cell disease - involving pain and burdensome treatment, is that they feel sorry for the child in anticipation of its suffering. And while children with Down's syndrome tend to have a happy disposition, many parents say that they themselves would not want to be mentally impaired. Thus many parents feel that they are doing what is best for the unborn child, if they do not allow it to be born with a serious genetic illness or other disability.

By contrast, once a child is born, few parents would ask for its life to be deliberately cut short in order to spare it future suffering. Admittedly, in some cases medical treatment may prove futile. In such situations the kindest thing to do may be to withhold burdensome treatment that no longer serves any therapeutic purpose but merely makes the child feel worse. However, to let the child die peacefully when there is no longer any hope is very different from deliberately taking its life.

In fact, it would seem that attitudes on the part of parents and the medical profession towards the unborn child are far less protective than those towards the infant. Thus the life of the infant and young child is often considered inviolable, whereas that of the unborn child often is not so regarded. And so, if the child is not yet born, many parents will allow its life to be deliberately taken. This readiness to abort the life of the unborn child may be based on a failure fully to recognise the continuity of life before and after birth, though many women who have abortions on ground of foetal abnormality admit that they are aborting a baby. Given that the unborn child is already a human child and our neighbour, not to treat it in the same way as the infant is inconsistent. In other words, parental readiness to abort the unborn child out of pity in view of its future suffering is, at least in part, to be explained by human emotional and intellectual shortcomings.

Burden to society and the family

Another kind of reason for preventing the births of disabled children is a social one. According to this kind of reasoning, disabled children are thought to be a useless burden on society, incurring extra costs related to their special medical and educational needs. This is the kind of reasoning espoused by proponents of eugenic thinking. Eugenic arguments in favour of cutting some lives short are based on the view that human life has no or little value, unless it conforms to certain standards of perfection. The standards in question may vary. They may be racial or they may relate to human abilities and health. Last century we saw many examples of eugenics based on race or tribal affiliation. As to the Nazis, they espoused eugenic arguments that were cast both in terms of the inferiority of certain races and in terms of the inferiority of people affected by illness or disability. What the standards of perfection specified by the proponents of eugenic arguments all have in common is a devaluation of certain human lives on the ground that they do not fulfil certain conditions that are thought necessary for a human life worthy of social acceptance and welcome.

Most eugenic thinking has been couched in terms of utilitarian assessments of the value of various kinds of human achievement, and the disvalue of lives which are seen as unproductive and as constituting burdens on society. Eugenic arguments for abortion on grounds of foetal abnormality belong to this kind, since they tend to be couched in terms of burdens and costs to society and families.

Thus national and large scale prenatal screening programmes have to a large extent been motivated by financial considerations, as is made clear by the cost-benefit calculations in terms of which they tend to be justified. Undergirding the reasoning in favour of these screening programmes is also the ideal of a society rid of many of the illnesses that face us today.

Down's syndrome

Since the 1970s when screening programmes to avoid the birth of children affected by Down's syndrome and neural tube defects were initially set up, economic advantages and disadvantages of such programmes have been a recurring topic in medical journals. To give an early example, an influential article published in the British Medical Journal (*BMJ*) back in 1976 analyses the economic benefits of a Down's syndrome screening programme for women in the West of Scotland (Hagard and Carter, *BMJ*, 1976, vol. 1, pages 753-756). The costs were estimated in terms of laboratory analyses, publicity, the procedure itself, genetic counselling, private transport and so forth. The savings were measured in terms of costs of institutional care of affected children, costs of special education, lost economic productivity on the part of mothers and the low economic return generated by the individuals themselves. In short, this was a purely utilitarian calculation based on financial costs to society. In terms of this kind of reasoning, the lives of some human beings are devalued on the ground that, from the perspective of society, they are not economically cost-effective. In more recent publications it is assumed that prenatal testing for Down's syndrome is cost-effective and so the emphasis is now on the efficacy of different tests in detecting the condition and on comparative analysis of their cost-effectiveness. A typical example is an article published in the *BMJ* on March 4th 2000, where the authors compare the detection rate and cost-effectiveness of the alpha-fetoprotein test with mid-pregnancy ultrasound screening. (David T Howe *et.al., BMJ*, 2000, vol. 320, pages 606-610).

Burdens for parents

However, when prenatal testing is discussed with parents, the emphasis is not on the costs to society of disabled individuals but rather, on the burdens and costs to the families caring for them. The present abortion law in Britain similarly emphasises the burdens imposed on mothers and families caring for children who for some reason or another are not wanted. Thus it is noteworthy that one of the grounds for abortion specified under British law is that the continuance of the pregnancy would involve risk to the mental health of the pregnant woman or any existing children or her family greater than if the pregnancy were terminated. And it should be pointed out that the concept of mental health in this clause tends to be liberally interpreted. The question is not normally whether the mother or any born children in her family would go mad, but rather whether the woman feels that she can cope with another baby in the light of her situation, including her family situation.

Of course, it is hardly surprising if pregnant women worry about their own future as well as that of their families. A disabled child or a child weakened by illness and needing extra attention and care makes great demands on the family; financial, mental and physical. The mother may have to give up work altogether, which may affect the family income and involve a certain amount of loneliness for her. She may have no time for other activities or be left so exhausted that it affects her social life. And the siblings of an affected child might receive less attention than they would if their brother or sister had not been there. Furthermore, the disabled child may require not only extra medical care but also special schooling, imposing extra financial costs on the family. Yes, a disabled child does bring certain burdens for its parents and family. However, our sympathy for parents of disabled children should not rule out sympathy for the disabled themselves.

Inconsistent treatment

As noted above, it is inconsistent to treat the unborn child differently from the child who has been born. Many people would go out of their way to help and accommodate children with disability, while they would be prepared to abort an unborn child affected by the very same condition. Not only is it not logical to make such a distinction between born and unborn life, but also it is a moral mistake to do so.

The Church teaches that each human being possesses the same basic human dignity irrespective of his or her abilities and disabilities or stage of life. Each child is equally a member of the human family, and hence each child deserves to be welcomed and cherished. Each one of us is a gift from God reflecting in our own unique way His image from the very first moment of life. Thus, as the Church teaches, human life is to be respected and protected from the time of conception. And this applies no less to the physically or mentally disabled than to the hale and healthy.

However, in secular societies there is no common understanding of the value of human life. For this reason the secular mind finds it difficult to perceive the objective and intrinsic value of human life. Thus the value of human life becomes a value in the eye of the beholder only. This tends to foster a utilitarian scale of values. And if the value of human life is measured in terms such as social utility, beauty, material riches or power, it can be difficult to appreciate that a disabled person may lead a fulfilled life.

But it should be noted that, while nobody would claim that disability or illness are good things in themselves, there is no denying that our society is greatly indebted to people who make demands on us. Not only is this true in the case of individual families, who often learn much from disabled members, but society at large is enriched by the disabled. Indeed, by calling for a response like that of the Good Samaritan (*Lk 10:30-37*), the weak, the dependent, the ill and disabled may teach us how to treat others as our neighbours. By so doing they make us more humane. They render our society a great service by helping us to act in line with the Gospel call for love of neighbour. For, by giving us an opportunity to serve and by teaching us how to serve, they can make our society more welcoming towards those in need and a more pleasant place for all of us. For all of us will at some stage, sooner or later, need the care or help of others. By calling out to us and making us respond to them, the disadvantaged or weaker members of the human family promote a society in which human dignity and value is not measured in terms of economic achievement, beauty, social status or power, but in which the inherent value and dignity of each human being is recognised. And this is the only kind of society in which each one of us has a chance of flourishing and feeling secure. Only in a society that respects each and every member irrespective of physical or mental disability, riches, power, social status, race or age, can we all live free from fear of being viewed as individuals whose lives are disposable or not worth living.

PRENATAL DIAGNOSIS:
SOCIAL AND PSYCHOLOGICAL ASPECTS

Possible psychological consequences

There is no denying that prenatal diagnosis in order to avoid the birth of children with disabilities has fundamental social and psychological consequences. Not only does the practice encourage the view that the unborn child is disposable, but the practice of testing confronts women with choices that they would often have preferred not to have faced and which may cause a high degree of anxiety about the child's state of health. In some cases it may cause heightened maternal anxiety about the health of the child even after its birth. Some women even say that prenatal diagnosis can foster a dualistic attitude on the part of women towards their own bodies and a denial of their pregnancy until they have test results.

In our society there is much talk of free reproductive choices. However, many of these so-called reproductive choices are less free than people suspect. The pregnant mother cannot choose whether or not to be offered tests. She is forced to choose between having, or not having, the tests that she is being offered and between declining, or accepting, the offer of abortion, if her child is found to be disabled. These are painful choices. The so-called control that is gained by prenatal testing and selective termination is gained at a cost. Many women resent being offered tests that serve no purpose in promoting their health or that of the baby. Even more do they resent being pressurised.

Take the case of amniocentesis to detect Down's syndrome, which is routinely offered to women 'at risk'. It tends to be presented by the medical profession as a means of giving the woman more control over her life. The woman is told that if the test is negative, it will be reassuring, whilst in the case of a positive test she will have the choice of preventing the birth of the affected child. Moreover, it is often pointed out that an abortion on grounds of foetal disability would soon give the woman a chance to undertake a new pregnancy. And some women complain that they have been more or less frankly told that it would be irresponsible not to have the test. However, in being offered the test, the woman is forced to make a choice, a choice that she might rather have avoided.

Indeed, the medical profession is not unaware of this. And given the psychological stress involved as well as the risks attached to invasive tests, such as amniocentesis and chorion villus sampling, doctors are in many cases reluctant to allow a woman to have such tests, unless she has indicated a preparedness to have an abortion, should her child be found to be disabled. Hence, pregnant mothers who have tests like amniocentesis to detect conditions such as Down's syndrome are usually prepared to consider an abortion if their child is found to be affected by the condition. This does not make their situation any easier for them. But it means that they know in advance of the test with what further choices they may be confronted. That is to say, the woman who is offered a test such as this, which is aimed at detecting foetal abnormality in order to give the mother the opportunity to opt for an abortion, would normally have been offered some kind of information or counselling about the possible outcomes of the test and about the options open.

By contrast, this is not always true of women who have routine ultrasound scans. Because the scan is non-invasive and considered harmless and offered routinely, it may confront women with unwelcome choices, for which they are ill prepared. Even the woman who has never contemplated having an abortion may be faced with the painful question whether she prefers to have an abortion or carry to term and give birth to a severely disabled baby. No test is innocent in the sense that it cannot lead to painful choices.

However, tests specifically aimed at detecting foetal abnormality tend to give rise to special anxieties. Not only will the pregnant mother worry about the discomfort that may be associated with the test or tests, but the test in question will heighten her awareness of the possibility that her child may be unwell. If she is contemplating the possibility of an abortion, the thought of that procedure will be a further cause of anxiety as will that of the loss of the child. Indeed, often the pregnancy of a woman in this kind of situation is very much wanted.

Women contemplating prenatal diagnosis the main aim of which is to avoid the birth of a handicapped child often hide their pregnancy until they have reassuring test results. This is not surprising. Rather more surprising is the finding that the pregnant woman sometimes pretends to herself that she is not really pregnant. But the reason for this is clear: the woman is seeking to avoid psychological pain. This is why the offer of a test such as amniocentesis may lead to a kind of self-deception and denial of the pregnancy until there are reassuring test results. For the woman does not want to invest emotionally in her pregnancy until she feels that she can count on the child. Her self-deception is a result of her anxiety, which is related to the fact that she may lose a wanted child. It was the American writer Barbara Katz Rothman who first drew public attention to the fact that some women who are offered an amniocentesis put their feelings on hold (Barbara Katz Rothman, *The Tentative Pregnancy*, London, 1988, pages 97-115). And to describe this phenomenon, Rothman coined a new term 'the tentative pregnancy'. As this term suggests, many pregnancies are not only concealed and kept secret until the woman has undergone prenatal tests and had tests that indicate that all is well, but in a sense the woman even hides her pregnancy from herself.

This said, most pregnant mothers, even those whose pregnancy was unplanned, recognise their baby in the sense that they have a natural tendency to do what is good for the baby and, for example, choose their diet more carefully than they usually would. And following a car crash, for example, they would seek medical attention to make sure the baby is all right. This is true even very early on in pregnancy well before the baby's kicks can be felt and even before the baby's heartbeat can be heard by the doctor or midwife.

Ethical and social implications of prenatal diagnosis

The practice of prenatal testing with a view to the possibility of abortion on grounds of foetal abnormality is inherently eugenic. This is the case even if the emphasis is on parental or maternal choice. Admittedly, eugenics has normally been associated with non-voluntary and state-sponsored sterilisations of the mentally handicapped or with outdated scientific ideas about human races. Thus the word eugenics has been more associated with force than with voluntary actions. But the subtle and not so subtle pressures on women to undergo prenatal tests also deserve to be described as eugenic. Even if the so-called reproductive choices involving prenatal diagnosis are voluntary, they are socially encouraged by ideological pressures. That is to say, prenatal diagnosis, in being sponsored by medical institutions and offered as a routine procedure to prevent the birth of disabled children, is a tool of social selection regulated by national legislation, and is hence eugenic.

However, there is an important difference between, for example, forced sterilisations and prenatal diagnosis inasmuch as in the case of prenatal diagnosis and selective abortion individual preferences and the social system often work together. Thus, while economic considerations were decisive when Britain, in the 1970s, initiated screening programmes to prevent the birth of children with neural tube defects and Down's syndrome, today many women themselves come forward and demand tests to avoid the birth of disabled children.

To be sure, tests are not actually imposed on women, even if women can come under strong pressure to have them. Also, women are not normally advised to have tests on the grounds that selective abortion of babies affected by Down's syndrome or other illnesses would involve national savings. Rather, medical doctors and midwives offer and advise women to have tests mainly because they think that such tests are in the women's or their family's best interest. Moreover, the emphasis is on non-directive counselling and informed reproductive choices. That is to say, women or couples are supposed to make up their own minds on the basis of information presented in a supposedly quite neutral fashion to them.

Nevertheless, the general ethos among the health professions promotes the idea that the availability of prenatal diagnosis and selective abortion is a blessing for women or couples. It is commonly argued that the reassurance provided by the availability of tests has allowed children to be born to thousands of parents at risk, who would otherwise not have contemplated starting a pregnancy. This is in addition to the argument that the mother and her family may be spared an enormous burden of care by avoiding the birth of a disabled child. It is also pointed out that the introduction of prenatal diagnosis and selective abortion has reduced the mortality rate of newborn babies with disabilities and improved over-all infant health.

Eugenic mentality

Another reflection - of quite a different kind - of the truth that our society is permeated with a eugenic attitude is the fact that in families with a genetic condition there is often a kind of guilt attached to the thought that the illness might be passed on to the next generation. Parents who already have a child with cystic fibrosis often feel that they have no right to pass the condition on to another child - and yet, at the same time, they may feel that they have the right to another child and, therefore, a right to avail themselves of prenatal diagnosis with a view to selection. Even if there is no previous history of the condition in the family, parents may feel guilty if they have a child with a condition such as cystic fibrosis or Down's syndrome. They may feel guilty vis-a-vis the child, vis-a-vis the rest of the family and vis-a-vis society at large. They may feel inadequate and think that it is their fault that the child is disabled. And this kind of guilt feeling is reinforced by the availability of prenatal diagnosis. For the availability of prenatal diagnosis means that many children born with a genetic or other disability need not have been born. The parents know this and they know that their friends and relatives know this.

In our society today it is not only the state machine as such that promotes eugenics. Rather the inherent ethos of society and the very availability of prenatal diagnosis promote eugenics. Quite simply, with the availability of prenatal diagnosis and the insistence on free parental choice, coupled with a widespread utilitarian outlook on life and a great concern about physical fitness, there is pressure on both doctors and parents to make sure that children are born healthy and, as a consequence, that unborn children are not born if they are not healthy. The very availability of prenatal diagnosis, together with these other attitudes, has promoted the idea that it is part of responsible parenthood to avoid the birth of a disabled child. In other words, it has promoted the idea that it is irresponsible to give birth to a child affected by a genetic illness or other disabling condition, if the condition might have been detected by prenatal diagnosis and if the parents failed to avail themselves of the same. As a result there is a vicious circle of pressure at play today, the pressure of an ideology that is inherently eugenic. The pressure is there for doctors and midwives to offer tests and for mothers to have them.

Conclusion

In well-off industrialised societies we now have the means to promote safer pregnancies and births than ever before. This is the positive side of our new technologies in obstetric care. However, there is also a dark side to these technologies: the births of many children are prevented by their means. This is because prenatal testing can be used either with a view to determining the health of the unborn child in order to guide the management of pregnancy towards a safe delivery, or it may be used with a view to selective abortion in order to avoid the birth of a disabled child.

In the first case, but not in the second, the aim is the therapeutic one of traditional Christian and Hippocratic medicine. In the middle ages, Christian medicine, which was often the prerogative of monks and nuns, encountered the Hippocratic tradition of medicine and embraced it, since it too expressed a great respect for human life. Thus the aim of Christian and Hippocratic medicine is to promote the health of the individual patient examined or treated, or if that is not possible, to seek to alleviate suffering - but never by getting rid of the patient. Medicine in the Christian and Hippocratic tradition respects the principle of the sanctity of human life, born and unborn. However, abortion represents alienation from the Christian and Hippocratic tradition of medicine, in which the ethos of patient-centred healthcare is rooted.

Thus prenatal testing undertaken in order to avoid the birth of a handicapped child is contrary to the age-old tradition of western medicine founded on Christian and Hippocratic values. Prenatal diagnosis undertaken in order to give the pregnant woman the option to terminate the pregnancy, if the child is disabled, fails to respect the principle of the sanctity of life. But medicine in the Christian and pro-life tradition of old is opposed to the idea of taking human life at any stage. While seeking to promote human health and ability, it does not measure human worth and dignity in these terms, but recognises the intrinsic value and dignity of each human being, irrespective of age, ability or state of health.

Further reading

Church documents

These documents are all available from the CTS.

Congregation for the Doctrine of the Faith, *Donum Vitae*, 1987 (published by the CTS as '*The Gift of Life*').
John Paul II, Apostolic Exhortation *Familiaris Consortio*, 1981.
Apostolic Letter *Mulieris Dignitatem* (*Dignity of Women*), 1988.
Letter to Families, 1994.
Encyclical Letter, *Evangelium Vitae* (*The Gospel of Life*), 1995.

Bioethics literature

Michael Banner, 'The Practice of Abortion: a Critique', in his *Christian Ethics and Contemporary Moral Problems*, Cambridge University Press, Cambridge 1999.
David King, 'Eugenic Tendencies in Modern Genetics', in Peter Doherty and Agneta Sutton (Eds.), *Man-Made Man: Ethical and Legal Issues in Genetics*, Dublin 1997, pages 71-82.
Gilbert Meilaender, *Bioethics: A Primer for Christians*, William B. Eerdmans, Grand Rapids, Michigan 1996.
Agneta Sutton, *Prenatal Diagnosis: Confronting the Ethical Issues*, Linacre Centre, London 1990.
Helen Watt, *Life and Death in Healthcare Ethics*, Routledge, London 2000.
Abortion, CTS and Linacre Centre, London 2001 (in the same series as the present booklet).

Useful contacts

Lejeune Clinic for Children with Down's Syndrome, Hospital of St John and St Elizabeth: 020 7289 8141.
Life: 01926 311511 (pregnancy and post-abortion counselling).

GLOSSARY

Alpha-fetoprotein: a protein present in the blood of the foetus, traces of which in the maternal blood may indicate a spinal defect.

Amniocentesis: the removal of amniotic fluid to test for foetal abnormality.

Amniotic fluid: fluid surrounding the foetus within the amniotic sac in the womb.

Antenatal: before birth.

Carrier: person with a faulty gene linked to a certain disorder. Carriers are not always affected themselves by the disorder in question but may pass it on to their children. Some disorders require two copies of the faulty gene for the child to be affected. This is the case with so-called recessive disorders.

Chorionic tissue: tissue surrounding the embryo containing embryonic cells.

Chorion villus sampling: the removal of chorionic tissue to test for foetal abnormality.

Chromosomes: microscopic bodies in the nuclei of cells containing the genes. In humans there are 23 pairs of chromosomes. In females they are numbered 1 to 22, while the last pair is described as XX; in males the last pair is described as XY.

Conception: the union of sperm and ovum (egg).

Cordocentesis: foetal blood sampling.

Cystic fibrosis: a genetic disorder common among people of European origin.

Dominant single gene disorder: a disorder due to a single faulty gene, where the risk of inheriting the disease from a parent carrying the gene is 50%.

Down's syndrome: a genetic abnormality due to the presence of an extra chromosome 21.

Duchenne muscular dystrophy: an hereditary disorder for which the gene is located on the X chromosome.

Embryo: unborn child from conception until the end of the second month.

Eugenics: an ideology according to which some human beings are seen as superior to others because of certain characteristics deemed especially desirable, coupled with certain policies to promote humans with the desired characteristics and eliminate those with the characteristics that are thought undesirable.

Foetus: the unborn child from the beginning of the third month to birth.

Fertilisation: conception.

Gene: the basic biological unit of heredity. The genes are situated on the chromosomes, and thus come in pairs, like the chromosomes themselves.

Haemophilia factor VIII: a bleeding disorder characterised by a failure of the blood to coagulate due to lack of clotting factor VIII.

Haemophilia factor IX: a bleeding disorder characterised by a failure of the blood to coagulate due to clotting factor IX.

HIV virus: the virus that causes AIDS.

Human chorionic gonadotropin (hCG): a component in the maternal blood, a high level of which suggests that the baby may have a chromosomal disorder.

Huntington disease: a genetic condition in which, during adult life, there is worsening involuntary movement and progressive dementia, and which leads eventually to death.

Invasive procedure: a procedure which involves entering the body with a syringe or other instrument.

In vitro fertilisation (IVF): the creation of an embryo outside the maternal body.

Malformation: irregular structure due to abnormal foetal development.

Neural tube defects: defects arising from protrusion of the brain or spinal cord.

Oestriol: a component in the maternal blood, low levels of which suggests that the baby is unwell.

Ovum: the female egg.

Placenta: the organ in the womb (of foetal origin) from which the foetus derives its nourishment via the umbilical cord.

Prenatal: before birth.

Pre-implantation diagnosis: diagnosis of a medical condition in the embryo created by *in vitro* fertilisation (IVF).

Recessive single gene disorder: a gene disorder resulting from a pair of faulty genes. If both parents are carriers of the particular faulty gene, the risk of inheriting the disorder is 25%.

Rhesus compatibility: see Rhesus disease.

Rhesus disease: foetal anaemia due to destruction of foetal blood cells by maternal antibodies. This can happen if the mother belongs to the rhesus negative and the foetus to the rhesus positive blood group.

Sex chromosomes: X and Y chromosomes. Females have two X chromosomes whereas males have one X chromosome and one Y chromosome.

Sex-linked disease: a disease inherited through a gene on an X-chromosome.

Sickle-cell disease: an hereditary form of anaemia, common among people of African origin.

Single gene disorder: an hereditary disorder linked to a single faulty gene.

Spina bifida: a condition involving the failure of the vertebrae or back bones to close, often resulting in paralysis of the lower part of the body.

Tay-Sachs disease: an inherited fatal disease. Death usually occurs within 18 months after birth.

Thalassaemia: an hereditary form of anaemia common in people of Mediterranean origin.

Therapeutic: healing, or otherwise concerned with treatment.

Ultrasound scan: a non-invasive test involving the visualisation of the foetus on a screen.

X-chromosome: see chromosomes.

Y-chromosome: see chromosomes.

Informative Catholic Reading

We hope that you have enjoyed reading this booklet.

If you would like to find out more about CTS booklets - we'll send you our free information pack and catalogue.

Please send us your details:

Name ....

Address ....

....

....

Postcode ....

Telephone...

Email ....

Send to: CTS, 40-46 Harleyford Road,
            Vauxhall, London
            SE11 5AY

Tel: 020 7640 0042
Fax: 020 7640 0046
Email: info@cts-online.org.uk